LITTLE BIG BOOK **PLUS**

Table of Contents

The Itsy Bitsy Spider 5
a story / song by Iza Trapani

The Itsy Bitsy Spider 32
a finger play

Spider Webs 33
an article from Your Big Backyard *magazine*

Where Are the Spiders? . . . 34
a map that shows where different spiders live

Spider 36
a poem by Aileen Fisher

Meet
Iza Trapani

Iza Trapani has always loved books for children. She says, "If you ever happened to see me in a waiting room, I would be the adult reading Dr. Seuss."

Now Ms. Trapani loves writing and illustrating her own books.

THE
ITSY BITSY
SPIDER

THE
ITSY BITSY
SPIDER

As told and illustrated by
Iza Trapani

HOUGHTON MIFFLIN COMPANY

BOSTON

ATLANTA   DALLAS   GENEVA, ILLINOIS   PALO ALTO   PRINCETON

*A huge thanks to Kim and Dan Adlerman for their
input and enthusiasm in producing this book*

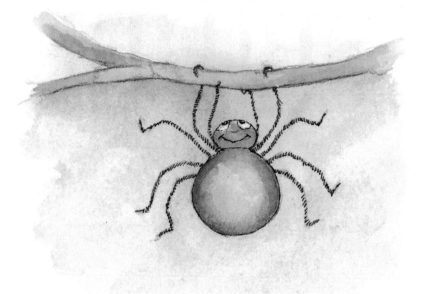

Acknowledgments

Grateful acknowledgment is made for use of the following material:

Text

1 *The Itsy Bitsy Spider,* retold and illustrated by Iza Trapani. Copyright © 1993 by Whispering Coyote Press. Reprinted by permission.
33 "Spiders," from October, Series II issue of *Your Big Backyard* magazine. Copyright © 1981 by the National Wildlife Federation. Reprinted by permission. **36** "Spider," from *Cricket in a Thicket,* by Aileen Fisher. Copyright © 1963 by Aileen Fisher. Reprinted by permission of the author.

Illustrations

32 Suçie Stevenson. **33** Doug Roy.

Photography

i Tony Scarpetta. **ii** Tracey Wheeler. **33** E. S. Ross. **34** © Bob Parks/The Wildlife Collection (t); © Animals Animals/George K. Bryce (b). **35** © Animals Animals/E. R. Degginger (t); © Animals Animals/Patti Murray (b). **36** The Metropolitan Museum of Art. Gift of Dr. and Mrs. Harold B. Bilsky, 1975 (1975.282.1h). Photograph by Bob Hanson.

1997 Impression

Houghton Mifflin Edition, 1996
Copyright © 1996 by Houghton Mifflin Company. All rights reserved.

Printed in the U.S.A.

ISBN 0-395-73160-7

10 11 12 13 14 15 - B - 98 97

FOR MY NIECES — BEATA,
EMILIA, AND ROSIE, WITH LOVE

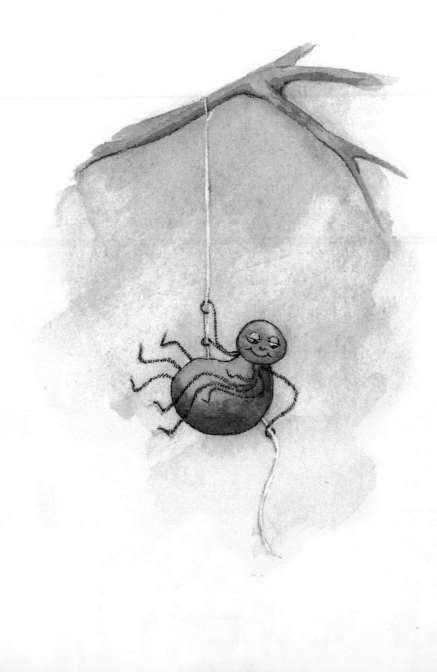

The itsy bitsy spider
Climbed up the waterspout.

5

Down came the rain
And washed the spider out.

Out came the sun
And dried up all the rain,
And the itsy bitsy spider
Climbed up the spout again.

The itsy bitsy spider
Climbed up the kitchen wall.

Swoosh! went the fan
And made the spider fall.

Off went the fan.
No longer did it blow.
So the itsy bitsy spider
Back up the wall did go.

The itsy bitsy spider
Climbed up the yellow pail.

In came a mouse
And flicked her with his tail.

Down fell the spider.
The mouse ran out the door.
Then the itsy bitsy spider
Climbed up the pail once more.

The itsy bitsy spider
Climbed up the rocking chair.

17

Up jumped a cat
And knocked her in the air.

19

Down plopped the cat
And when he was asleep,
The itsy bitsy spider
Back up the chair did creep.

The itsy bitsy spider
Climbed up the maple tree.

She slipped on some dew
And landed next to me.

22

Out came the sun
And when the tree was dry,
The itsy bitsy spider
Gave it one more try.

The itsy bitsy spider
Climbed up without a stop.

She spun a silky web
Right at the very top.

She wove and she spun
And when her web was done,

28

The itsy bitsy spider
Rested in the sun.

The   it - sy bit - sy spi - der Climbed up   the wa - ter - spout.

Down   came the rain   And   washed the spi - der out.

Out   came the sun   And   dried up all   the rain, And   the

it - sy bit - sy spi - der   Climbed up   the spout a - gain.

2. The itsy bitsy spider
   Climbed up the kitchen wall.
   Swoosh! went the fan
   And made the spider fall.
   Off went the fan.
   No longer did it blow.
   So the itsy bitsy spider
   Back up the wall did go.

3. The itsy bitsy spider
   Climbed up the yellow pail.
   In came a mouse
   And flicked her with his tail.
   Down fell the spider.
   The mouse ran out the door.
   Then the itsy bitsy spider
   Climbed up the pail once more.

4. The itsy bitsy spider
   Climbed up the rocking chair.
   Up jumped a cat
   And knocked her in the air.
   Down plopped the cat
   And when he was asleep,
   The itsy bitsy spider
   Back up the chair did creep.

5. The itsy bitsy spider
   Climbed up the maple tree.
   She slipped on some dew
   And landed next to me.
   Out came the sun
   And when the tree was dry,
   The itsy bitsy spider
   Gave it one more try.

6. The itsy bitsy spider
   Climbed up without a stop.
   She spun a silky web
   Right at the very top.
   She wove and she spun
   And when her web was done,
   The itsy bitsy spider
   Rested in the sun.

The Itsy Bitsy Spider

1

The itsy bitsy spider
Climbed up the waterspout.

2

Down came the rain

3

And washed the spider out.

4

Out came the sun

5

And dried up all the rain.

6

And the itsy bitsy spider
Climbed up the spout again.

Spider Webs

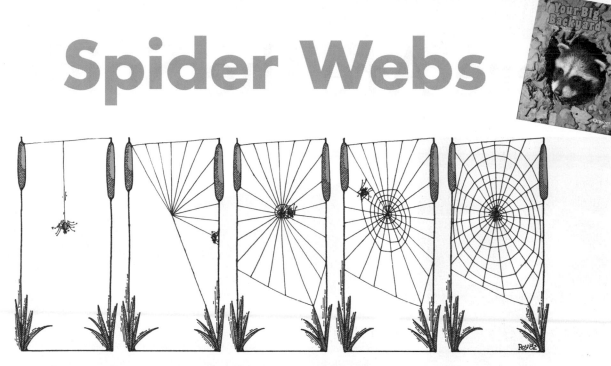

Look how this spider weaves its web.

Where Are the Spiders?

**Orb-Weaving
Spider
California**

**Green Lynx
Spider
Arizona**

34

**Jumping Spider
New Jersey**

**Red and Black
Argiope Spider
Florida**

35

a spider from the album *Flowers and Birds* by Taki Katei

蜘蛛

Spider

I saw a little Spider
with the smartest spider head:
she made — somewhere inside her —
a magic silken thread.

I saw her sliding down it.
She dangled in the air.
I saw her climbing up it
and pulling up each stair.

She made it look so easy
I wished all day I knew
how *I* could spin a magic thread
so I could dangle too.

by Aileen Fisher